From the inner city to the suburbs to the hills of South Dakota, young people will see themselves, and hear their own powerful voices in the pages of Tony Medina's book. Talking trash. Spitting wisdom. Whispering into God's ear or singing to the world. Medina's young voices offer a window into the insight, creativity and wonder of American youth. Be prepared for students to enjoy every delicious word.

—Sharon G. Flake
author of *The Skin I'm In* and *Pinned*

Medina's The President Looks Like Me *proves that powerful poetry can be enlightening, inspirational and fun. These diverse poems resonate with the audacity of youth and cool. A must read for teens and tweens.*

—Kwame Alexander, 2012 NAACP Image Award Nominee,
author of *Acoustic Rooster and his Barnyard Band* with
NY Times Bestselling Illustrator, Tim Bowers

Tony Medina has the uncanny ability and artistry to write in the voices of children—their thoughts, their fears, and above all, their hopes and dreams. I love reading his wonderful work!

—Marilyn Singer, author of *Mirror Mirror* (Dutton)

In Tony Medina's The President Looks Like Me, *rhythmic voices ring out celebrating cultural mixtures of church music, John Coltrane, Celia Cruz and "hip-hop" crazy. Images of Sunday soul food dinners, piragua carts, watermelon, classroom activities, and everyday street scenes resonate through the voices of America's children and are familiar to those who have grown up in a big city. In the spirit of Lucille Clifton's "Good Times," Medina's multicultural poems make this book enjoyable to read, proud to celebrate, and they loudly proclaim that "the president really does look like me."*

—Dr. Nancy D. Tolson, Mitchell College
author of *Black Children's Literature Got De Blues:
the Creativity of Black Writers and Illustrators*

THE PRESIDENT LOOKS LIKE ME

& OTHER POEMS

TONY MEDINA

http://justusbooks.com

ISBN 978 1-933491-94-3
e-ISBN 978 1-933491-93-6
Cover and interior illustrations copyright © 2013 by Mansa K. Mussa
Cover Design by 2ndChapter
Printed in USA

Hold fast to dreams.

—Langston Hughes

CONTENTS

PREFACE

The election of Barack Obama as the first African-American president of the United States marked a pivotal point in the history of a nation often preoccupied with race, color and identity. Millions of people around the world have been inspired by Mr. Obama's historic victory and his personal story of determination and success—especially children of color.

In *The President Looks Like Me and Other Poems*, Tony Medina celebrates the diversity that President Obama symbolizes through poems that are multiculural in scope and wide-ranging in style. With distinctly urban settings and flavor, this collection covers a myriad of themes including childhood, family, friendship, identity, spirituality, social justice and Hip Hop. Medina's poems realistically capture the impact of what it means to be young in a complex world. Yet, they also offer hope—hope that resounds more prominently when a child of color can say, "the president looks like me."

*For my aunt, Rachel Frances Medina Rivera,
for her many names and many talents*

PART ONE
THE PRESIDENT LOOKS LIKE ME

I am America. I am the part you won't recognize.

—Muhammad Ali

THE PRESIDENT LOOKS LIKE ME

The President looks like me
The President is brown like me
His hair is like my hair—
Tightly curled, neatly trimmed and free
He has a name like me
He plays b-ball too
He is mad cool
The President makes me
Want to stay in school
Go to college so one day
I can achieve my dreams
Make them a reality

Granddad said he could not believe
He'd live to see the day
That we would have
A Black President
When Barack Obama
Put his hand on the Bible
During his inauguration
On that coldest of the coolest day
I saw a tear in my
Granddad's eye
A smile so wide
It made me want to fly

GRANDMA'S HANDS

Grandma's hands are
Always holding
Something

Needles and thread
Beads or bread
Broom or bedspread

They are soft
Smooth shiny
Like leather

With veins that
Move when you
Touch

Knuckles like knots
That hurt her
So much

It's hard for her to
Hold a brush or
Open bottles and cans

But easy when
She cups
My face

To wipe my tears
Or hold my hand
To chase my fears

Grandma's hands
Are always
Holding me
When they can

TONY MEDINA

3

UNCLE PEPE

Uncle Pepe
Had a face
Like a dandelion
His cheeks speckled
Into a million
Gray stubbles sharp
As sandpaper sheets
Two teeth parted
By a world
Was his smile
His laughter
Brought down
A thunder
From the clouds
In his chest
He walked
The stairs
Slowly
Then after
Needed rest

When your head
Was too short
To see over
The tabletop
He'd bounce you
On his knee
Dazzle you with
Lemon and lime
Lollipops
Feed you
Cakes, cereal,
Raspberries
'Til your face
Turned red
On this memory
And the music
In his eyes
I am fed
Not the rainy days
Of never seeing him
Again instead

SUNDAYS

Sundays we go to church
Mama wakes me early
I wash and
Put on my dress clothes
My shiny patent leather shoes

Mama cooks a light breakfast
'Cause after church we really
Throw down with baked chicken
Mac and cheese, big buttery biscuits
Piles of mashed potatoes and black-eyed peas
With peach cobbler and sweet potato pie
Tastes so sweet it makes you cry—
Hallelujah!

Sundays we go to church
I sing in the choir
We stand behind our pastor
He gives his sermon that inspires
Us to do good things for other people
Which is called God's work
The congregation says—
Amen!

Mr. Russell plays his piano
My sister sings her sweet solo
Hands raise up in the air
My auntie and our neighbor Miss Rosie
Get the Holy Ghost
Everybody shouts—
Hallelujah! Hallelujah!
Amen!

My stomach starts to grumble
My nose catches the Holy Spirit
Of all that yummy smelling soul food
The pastor says, *Let us all eat!*
Come share in this bountiful feast…
My tummy shouts out
Hallelujah!
Hallelujah!

STAND-IN FATHER

Can your uncle be like a stand-in father
When yours is gone and you don't know where he's at?
Can he come pick you up and make you gather
Your baseball glove and brand new baseball bat

Sundays while he hits fly balls for you to catch?
Then turns around pitching to you underhand
While you hit homeruns as if there were no match
Saying, "There you go again, my little man."

Can your uncle be there when you need to talk
About guy things your mom just won't understand
During video games or out for a walk
Talking about girls and grownup stuff man-to-man?

Can your uncle be there whenever he can
Like a father teaching you to be a man?

RHYME TIME

There is an old man
With cardboard feet
He pushes a shopping cart
Looking for food to eat

He pushes his raggedy rickety cart
Through back alleys and side streets
Picking through trash cans
Weary of dirty meat

His feet hurt, his stomach growls
He does not feel too neat
People act like he isn't there
Though their stares give off mad heat

They turn their noses up at him
Which makes him feel defeat
Unlike the bullets and bombs
He dodged when he was in wartime's reach

I see him on my way to school
Try to be discreet
When I fumble through my lunch bag
To slide him my PB&J with a fuzzy peach

As he sleeps slumped and snoring like a log
In the damp dirty alley on the cold concrete
His breath rattles and rumbles through him
Like ping pong balls from his head to his feet

MY FAVORITE THINGS

John Coltrane's version of this tune
A dark blue sky with a big full moon
That hangs so low I could touch it with a broom
Stars I could see with a telescope from my room
Ice cold watermelon on a hot summer day
Riding on the back of pickup trucks full of hay
Baked fish instead of red meat
Hot chocolate in the winter and Timbs to warm my feet
Playing cards with people who don't cheat

Church services that don't last too too long
Stevie Wonder's "Happy Birthday" song
An Aretha Franklin hit
James Brown's split
Michael Jackson's Moonwalk and spin
When The Yankees win
Manga with two stories instead of one
My brown skin soaking up the sun
At Dave & Busters eating and having fun
Playing Spades with my uncle Raymond

My aunts Vilma and Josie watching my aunt Rachel
Paint pictures of me
When the older dudes call me Cool Breeze
Mac & cheese
When I play football and don't wheeze

When my mother bakes a cake and I get to lick the spoon
Catching lightning bugs in June
Chocolate-covered jelly rings
Fried green tomatoes
Black-eyed peas on the dinner table
The story of Cain and Abel
When Jonah finally gets out of the whale
When I get my report card and I didn't fail

Gym and lunch
In the play yard with cookies or chips to munch
Relay races when I'm running fast
When our car doesn't break down or run out of gas

Long Johns in the winter
Long basketball trunks in the summer
Peanut butter and jelly on wheat bread
Buffalo wings with french fries drenched in ketchup
Sprinkled with curry powder
Jamaican beef patties
Pizza, sushi and Chinese food
Samosas, Mulligatawny or Matzo ball soup
Spaghettios

Winning spelling bees
Wearing my black jeans
Platanos and collard greens
Salsa music on Saturdays all night long
With Tito Puente y Celia Cruz
Bob Marley's reggae songs
Candy canes, caramel apples and grape juice
Bowling, wiffle ball
The elephants at the zoo

Playing the drums with pots and spoons
Nerf basketball off the back of the door of my room
The smell of incense and oils
Muslim prayers coming from mosque loudspeakers
Reading sci-fi books
Going to the Natural History Museum to see dinosaurs
Making funny faces through the shark tank at the aquarium
Batman, Spiderman and Superman cartoons
Playing video games while listening to I-tunes
Rock climbing when my mom allows
Fancy dancers at powwows

Burying my dad up to his neck at the beach
Racing big waves, staying out of their reach
Learning to dive and swim in the big people's pool
Blowing bubbles with washing detergent and soap
Taking a bubble bath with my mother's shampoo
Getting my haircut with a part and my initials
Or letting my big sister braid my long curls
Playing hopscotch or Double Dutch and beating the girls
Dominoes with my granddad while listening to jazz
Falafels and waffles and blueberry pancakes piled to the moon
Chocolate pudding with whipped cream

Pineapple chunks buried in Jello
My Pittsburgh Steelers jersey that's black and yellow
When my mom plays Sade to make her mellow
Sneakers instead of dress shoes
Playing chess when I don't lose
Putting the star atop the Christmas tree
Anything that's free

Learning new languages and reading about other countries
Klondike bars, Twizzlers and hot buttered popcorn at the movies
Pretzels with mustard when I get hungry
Blue corn tortilla chips with guacamole
Albizu Campos, Cesar Chavez, Crazy Horse
Freedom fighters I learn about in history class
President Obama and Supreme Court Justice Sotomayor
Wearing a baseball cap sideways like the older fellas do
Eating at a restaurant—not the drive-thru

Church bus trips to amusement park rides
Going through a safari with a tour guide
Mom rubbing Vicks on my chest when I'm sick
Cinnamon candlesticks
Birthday piñatas filled with candies and toys
Playing hide-and-go seek
Listening to my grandpa speak

Playing stickball with mop handles and broomsticks
Old cars my dad teaches me how to fix

Riding go-carts and bumper cars
Visiting my grandma
Singing in the church choir
At camp rubbing two sticks to make fire
Making art sculptures out of wire
Water balloon and snowball fights
In the park flying kites
Cats that don't scratch, dogs that don't bite
Carrying my baby sister when she was light
When mom and dad don't fight
Making a snowman with my best friend Stan
Juggling with my feet while rocking a headstand

PART TWO
HIP HOP CRAZY

Every great dream begins with a dreamer.

—Harriet Tubman

HIP HOP CRAZY

In the mirror
    I make believe
I'm a rapper
    I rhyme with ease

I turn a sneeze
    Into a breeze
I freestyle flow
    Like on the radio

Everybody say, *Hey!*
    Everybody go, *Ho!*
A rapper, a rapper   A tap,
    Tap tapper

With my pop's
    Shades
And my mama's
    Hairbrush

A baseball cap
    On my head, I push
Back or to the side
    As I glide and slide

Sing *Hip Hop*
    Hippity Hop
And you don't stop
    Don't stop

STREET CORNERS

Street corners are not a place to be
Wasting time watching life spin away from me

Don't count on me being nobody's fool
Sleeping all day, dropping out of school

Running the streets all night worrying
My mama half to death

Turning my life into a mess
Having her wonder if I'm doing drugs

Having her wonder if I'm hanging with thugs
I won't spend my days clocking cop cars

Playing Russian roulette with my life
Ending up behind bars

Street corners are not a place to be
Wasting time wallowing in misery

Finding an escape in a cheap quick high
Killing time watching planes go by

My future I hold in the palm of my hand
March to my own beat, I'm my own man

I Am From

I am from
Break dance beats
And African heat
Cardboard on
City streets

I am from
Ambulances wailing
All hours of the night
Like a baby that needs changing
Or a bottle in sight

From graffiti eulogies
For drug dealers
That got shot
Or drive-by victims
Who died on the spot

I am from
Mothers
Staring out the window
Wondering where
Their kids are at

Fathers
Banging on the door
With a baseball bat
I am from all the sad, sad songs
On the radio

That little glimmer of hope
That makes you glow
And grow
And go
For yours

I am from
Cars that cough
Grandmas that snore
In the middle of church
Praying for Jesus to take them off

To a better place
Without arthritis
Or heart pills
Without no money
And doctor bills

I am from
Homeless living on the street
Sleeping on park benches
Stretched out on concrete
Atop street graters for heat

From a stone cold world
With so much to eat
But starving people
With canned cat food
For meat

At the Bottom of His Father's Secret Drawer

In the nightstand by his bedroom window
Rodney got a gun he saw his father hide there once
For burglars and intruders creeping around the house

There were bullets in the chamber
The barrel looked like a clenched fist
It was heavy as his football trophy

He hid it in his book bag
Took it to school to show off to his friends
But when he pulled it from his bag

His finger slipped and pressed the trigger
A sound popped out so loud
Like a firecracker tossed in a dumpster

A thunderclap from a lightning cloud
Going off in his hand ringing in his ear
So hard he couldn't hear

When the noise damped down
The smoke cleared out
A girl was on the floor clutching her chest

Trying to keep from
Spilling a bucket of blood
Where she was shot

BREAK DANCER

                              Card
                              board
                              be my
Magic
          Carpet—

     Feets don't
                         Fail
Me now!
               As I   B r E a K
Kick
     & Swing

          S p i n n i n g on
               My
     Back

     Holding   back
     My   legs

          Stopping
in   mid

     Move-
          Ment
                    To

Strike
          A

                    P o s e

TONY MEDINA
21

CARDBOARD CANTICLE

From a piece
   Of Cardboard
Stretched along concrete
   Streets
I join the cosmos
   Spinning my body
Into an asteroid
   Kicking my legs
Like propellers
   Standing on my head
Rotating like a top
   Even the wind
Has to stop
   To notice
As I chop it
   Down
Like a headhunting
   Helicopter
On projects' schoolyard
   Ground

Made sacred by
    B-boy sheer force
And grace
    Manipulating gravity
Slapboxing space with
    The skill
To escape
    These mean streets
Where I'm
    Raised and
Where I come from
    To push
Me up
    And out
Through
    The stratosphere
Among planets
    Like Venus,
Neptune, Mars
    High-fivin' stars

I Love to Rap

I love to rap
I love to rhyme
My favorite rappers
Are always on time:

Tupac, Mos Def,
Common, Lupe, Talib Kweli
Never talk smack
About girls or guns

Or act silly and fake
Their rhymes are serious
As a heart attack
About uplifting the Black race

Not being a disgrace
To their grandmothers
Matter of fact
They never get left back

I carry them around
In my head most times
When I'm in class
And it seems like I am hazy

Having my teacher say—
Do your math!
I'm working on my own rhymes
Working on what I have to say

About me, my block
My community
About my grandmother
My friends and family

But don't get me wrong
I'm not always in a song
I always get my schoolwork done
'Cause I'm not lazy

I'm just hip hop crazy

ON MY BLOCK

On my block
They have drugs
And thugs hanging out
On the corner
Who shoot you
Not only with their eyes
But with a gun
Just for stepping
On their shoe
Or bumping into them

On my block
We don't even
Have a park
To play
And when our ball
Rolls out
In the street
Cars come by
And run over
Our feet

On my block
The only thing that's good
Is in the summertime
When the johnnie pump
Is on and we
Jump and play
In the spray the
Can makes shooting
Water on us
When it's hot outside

HIP HOP YOU DON'T STOP

I am always doing that which I cannot do
in order that I may learn how to do it.
—from a Fortune Cookie

The DJ
Imagine making records spin like planets under your skin
　　Hands so swift and smooth looking for the perfect groove
Before there were CDs, DJs were the ones making
　　Vinyl wax music collages for everybody to jump up and move
One record sound sewn into another like your grandma's quilt
　　In a galaxy of milk crate record songs hip hop was built

The MC
Rapping and rhyming words so fast
　　I mix English with Spanish and Creole
Hip Hop Reggaeton flies out my mouth in a flash
　　American-born but from the Islands, I keep it real
I talk about who I am and where I'm from to rock the show
　　Rocking my triple tongue yo-yo, I stay on beat with my flow

The Break Dancer
Break dancing on cardboard
　　Kick-spinning like a whip-whirling star
A top pulled by a kite string cord
　　Hands and arms locked like the jack on a car
Twirling across the floor like a windmill
　　Legs gyrating breeze making everybody feel chill

The Graffiti Artist
Some names are scribbled into Krylon spraypaint screams
　　On buildings and benches like a big angry *Act Like You Know*
While others glow like bubble letters of multicolored dreams
　　Along trains winding through the city like a floating art show
Some think graffiti is made by vandals whose words are mad odd
　　But we be spraypaint Picassos flying our colors up to God

PART THREE
DEAR GOD

*My hope for my children must be
that they respond to the still, small
voice of God in their own hearts.*

—Andrew Young

DEAR GOD

Why are there so many wars
Abandoned burnt-out houses
With no doors

Why do people fight and shout
Isn't peace and love what we're
Supposed to be about

What about people
Who live out in the cold
Broke brick ones who are
Supposed to be young
But look so old

People who go hungry
Discarded ones who get
Swallowed by the earth

Dear God
Thank you for the blue skies
And the moon and the stars
That stretch and smile
Throughout the night

Thank you for bringing
The sun each day
Thank you for the flowers
Thirsty for rain

But please, God
Can you make people care more
And share more
Instead of making all this pain

Hurricane Katrina Haiku

People on buildings
Knee-deep in water…scared
God must be crying

HAIKU FOR THREE VOICES

I read the Torah
    My God is called Jehovah
        I pray to Allah

On Sunday we fast
       On Saturday we visit
              We kneel on carpets

                        Are prayers like wings?
                  Attached to the same body?
           Flying up to God?

Prayers are petals
    Religion is a flower
        We hold up to God

Tanka for My Dad

Clasped hands pray for peace
    Remember when Daddy left

Hoping he comes back

    So we can finish the score
Of games played before the war

POEM FROM HARLEM TO HAITI

There are kids under bricks
People with steel poles and sticks
Trying to free old folks who are sick

From the dust the earth kicked
After it split
In Haiti, in Haiti

Reminding me of New Orleans
When Hurricane Katrina
Flooded all the people

Stuck like glue in the
Mud and goo
Of government half-step

It makes me so sad it sickens me
To see our people suffer so
But I can't sit back

Watch people die on TV
I gotta get up, go—
Raise some money to help

Raise my people in Haiti
In New Orleans and Mississippi
Here in Harlem

Newark
Camden
Wherever they may be

There are kids under bricks
Old folks who are sick
Like my pastor says

Quoting Moses—*Let my people go!*
I say the same to earthquakes
Hurricanes and tsunamis

To rich folks
Governments
That do not care

'Cause I'm on the go
Making sure
My people grow

A Mother's Prayer

My mother sends me out in the world,
Clutching her black Bible and black rosary
I round the corner and feel her eyes
Through the curtain, her breath
Heavy, trails me like a second backpack,
Whispering to me telepathically, *Come*
Back safely, come back safely, come back

My mother spends the day busying herself
With chores and appointments and things
To do to keep from thinking thoughts
That mothers think when their sons
Go out into the world like homing pigeons

DEAR MAMA

I did what you said,
I wore my shirt tucked in my pants.
I looked both ways crossing the street.
I said *yes ma'am* and *no ma'am*
when spoken to. I can't understand
what went wrong. I just went into
the store to get some candy
and the man behind the counter
kept watching me as I went through
the aisles looking for chips and a soda.
Then he started accusing me of taking stuff,
asking me what do I have in my bag. I told him
nicely, all I have are books and my Gameboy,
but he called me a liar and grabbed at my bag,
yelling at me to open it. He called the cops
even though all that fell out were books and paper
and my Gambeboy that broke. The cops didn't believe me.
They even put me in handcuffs and took me to the station,
scaring me into signing a letter saying I took stuff.
Do you believe me, Mama?

The World Is a Choir

You step on my shoe
   I won't hit you

I'll wait for an apology
   If you diss me

I won't let you dismiss me
   I'll let you know how I feel

We should learn to get along
   We may not sing the same song

If the world is a choir
   We should at least be in tune

There's no need to solve problems
   With clenched fists

Anger is not the answer
   Bullying just ain't cool

Like my granddad says
   We need to be more creative

You step on my shoe
   I won't cut my eyes at you

I'll give you the benefit
   Of the doubt—no doubt

I'll forgive you your trespass
   Pray this peace will last

PART FOUR
TODAY
I LEARNED

*The point is not to payback
kindness but to pass it on.*

—Julia Alvarez

TODAY I LEARNED

Today I learned
About polar bears

Living on polar ice caps
(Which are not cool hats)

But big old sheets of ice
Called glaciers

From way back in the Ice Age
Beautiful polar bears

Live there in the Arctic
In freezing weather

But now are drowning
Because their ice caps

Are melting
From global warming

From all the heat we create—
Even from eating meat

How the pollution we make
Is trapped in the atmosphere

Like a giant popcorn bag
Making it hotter and hotter

Where it's supposed to be cold
Mixing up all the seasons

'Til bumblebees die
Because they can't fly

Bump and buzz around
Flowers that haven't bloomed

Today I learned if we don't stop
Polluting our planet, we're doomed

WHAT IF THERE WERE NO TREES

What if there were no trees
With green, green leaves?
Or honeybees?
Or air to breathe?

What if the ocean was full of oil
Instead of water?
And the fish could not swim?
And boats could not float?

What if the earth had
So much trash
It made you sneeze, wheeze
And breakout in a rash?

What if birds would crash,
Falling out of the sky?
Or the red-eyed sun had
A black eye?

Would it make you sad
You were so reckless?
Would it make you
Be more careful

When you throw trash
On the ground
Not in garbage cans
Or recycling bins?

Would it make you
Want to save water
Conserve energy—
Be more helpful

If it got so bad you
Couldn't stand it?
Would it make you
Want to save the planet?

ANTHILL AT MY HEEL

An anthill appeared at the tip of my shoe
Where ants crawled feverishly, spreading

Like spilled oil around to the heel
Of my tennis shoe,

Moving about like grown-ups
During morning rush hour

On their way to work in cars,
Climbing in and out of subways.

I watched them lug around
A piece of bread, haul off an orange peel,

Working together, ignoring my heel
As if it were a building that suddenly appeared.

I stood still as a statue, making sure not to
Move one inch of my shoe

Or risk creating an earthquake or
Avalanche of scattering ants.

I even tried holding my breath
To will myself completely still

But the ants started marching up
The backend of my tennis shoe

Quickly making it to my once
White but suddenly black sock

When they began to bite, going
On the attack.

What did these ants discover? My sneaker,
My sock, my ankle and shin,

As if I were a hunk of day-old bread,
Or a dried-out, discarded watermelon rind.

Before they could make it further
Uphill toward my behind,

I hauled off screeching, leaving the
Startled ants something else to find.

THESE BIG COMPANIES MAKE ME MAD
(AFTER WATCHING A MOVIE IN CLASS)

These big companies make me mad
They make me think about
How they steal peoples' land
How they gobble up trees in the rainforest
With machines that look like
They're eating broccoli

Chopping them to their knees
Without any rest
Until there aren't any left to shade
Or any life in the forest
Like bees, centerpedes, iguanas,
Monkeys, ants, spiders, parrots—
Even tiger lilies

Until we start to sneeze and freeze
With tight heavy leaden pains in our chests
From these greedy pollution bullies
Pushing native cultures off their land
And birds out of their nests

PART FIVE
WEEKENDS ARE
MY FAVORITE TIME

Everything you can imagine is real.

—Pablo Picasso

FALL

Like when summer comes
To an end
How amusement parks and pools
Quickly put up signs that say
Come back next year, my friend!

Like when a leaf turns
Brown orange yellow
How a rough wind snatches it up
As if to say—*Hello!*

Like when your knee
Bangs and scrapes along
Playground teeth
How your mother's eyes get big
At the sight of peeled-back skin
Hanging and clinging to your
Beige school pants turning red

Like when the wind starts
Getting a stank attitude
Commanding you to wear sweaters
Sometimes scarves to escape its cruel cool

Like when the street
Becomes a bowl of chips
How dried-up leaves
Crunch beneath your feet

Like when you go chasing
After a windswept ball
That bounces off the tip of your
Glove—just out of reach

Like when a draft whips
Through your room
Like snow swept in on a broom
Even though it's not cold enough
For your breath to fog the window

But you still freeze
Waking with a sneeze

HAIKU—BLESS YOU!

When I catch a cold,
    I cough my head off, my eyes
Get watery red.

    When I cough and sneeze
My head bursts like a balloon—
    Parachute nostrils.

I can barely breathe—
    Like two marshmallow pillows
Replaced my strained lungs.

    When I catch a cold
I always get a fever
    Which leads to asthma.

Asthma makes me wheeze.
    Wheezing is the sound wind makes
Going through tunnels.

    When I wheeze I think
Everybody can hear
    My wind tunnel nose.

Like I'm the music
    In a big horror movie—
The sound monsters make!

When I catch a cold
It's like I'm the star in my
    Own scary movie.

A runaway nose.
    Tissues piled to the ceiling.
My nostrils peeling.

    A cold makes me sick.
A cold is a bad feeling.
    A cold is not nice.

But my teacher says
    Colds help your body fight
Germs that invade you.

    Maybe colds are not
So bad after all—but they
    Shouldn't stay so long!

Colds are like guests that
    Do not ever leave until
You cough and you sneeze!

    The only good thing
About catching a cold is
    Mom pampering me.

WINTER

Winter
And the skinny
Projects trees
Stick out the
Soil and concrete
Like Popsicle sticks
Outside my window

Winter
And the leaves
Are stripped from
Their bony branches
Making the trees look
Like scarecrows
Outside my window

Winter
And the wind that whips
Its way between the buildings
Whistle through my ribcage
And lungs like cobwebs when
I jump on the bed to stare
Outside my window

Winter
And the sky
Smears its pasty gray
Across the red bricks
Until all is a pale blur
Dull as dirty snow
Outside my window

Winter
And my grandmother
Rubs Vicks
On my paper chest
While the other
Kids play
Outside my window

Winter
And the wind
Shakes the skinny trees
Where the other kids
Race and jump and scream
Between the scattered leaves
Outside my window

SPRING

When birds sing
Bees sting
Sunlight beams

Snow starts dripping
Flowers start opening
Butterflies spread wings

Rain clings
Leaves green
Grass gleams

Everything's
Warm and shiny
Happiness blings

Off buildings
Windows
Cars hoods that shine

Spring
When the sun
Stays out longer

We no longer
Have to wear
Big bulky coats

Once bundling us up
But now we get to go out
To play in the park

On the monkey bars
On swings
On the seesaw

To slide in
The sandbox where
We dive head first

Spring
When we run after
The ice cream truck

Duck
At the sight
Of bumblebees

Where Mama
Makes us wear our
Raincoats

Put on galoshes
Splash in play-
Ground puddles

When we chase each other
All over saying
Tag! You're it!

ODE TO POTATO CHIPS

A bag of chips
Filled with hot air
Is fun to pop
Open when you
Have to have some
Slices of sun
To lay on your
Tongue.

Flying saucers
Float out of the
Bag into your
Waiting mouth
That waters
With anticipation
Like a puppy
Waiting for his biscuit.

Oh the salty tang
Crispy snap
Is half the fun
When you try
So hard
To just have one
How you always
Lose on purpose.

Potato chips
Are thin lips
You dip into a
Bowl of salsa,
Guacamole or
French onion dip—

Sometimes people trip
Trying to get a chip!
Sometimes they miss
The bowl of dip completely
Knock over the bag
Which is a drag
When there are no more chips
'Cause somebody crunched them
Into the grooves of the bottom
Of their tennis shoes,

Then you have to take a trip
To a 24-hour store
Which makes you sore
Until you get your hands
On another bag
To pop with both hands
As the potato chip air
Lifts you up into the air.

PIRAGUA

A cathedral
Of ice
Crowned in
Sweet sticky
Rainbow delight
Shinier than
The Reverend's
Gold tooth smile
Cadillac chrome rims
On a sunny Sunday
That makes
Your forehead
Hot and wet
With curly
Hairs that
Frizz up from
Running
Jumping
Singing and
Screaming
Tag you're it!

Brown and red
In the mustard
Yellow sun
With a sweaty
Tongue you
Race to the
Piragua cart
For your ice
Cold syrupy
Sunrise for
Your round
Rainbow upside
Down pyramid surprise
Of orange
Grape cherry coconut
Tamarindo lindo
As the tan
On your face
And hands

Every Barrio
Has a piragua
Cart that
Stays in
One spot
All day
Like grandma
At the window
Praying and
Surveying or a
Reliable aunt
Moving from
Block to block
Drawing kids and
Grownups out
Like a slow motion
Mister Softee
Without the
Monotonous music
Of a windup box

The piragua cart
Blares salsa
Blasts merengue
From an old beat-up
Rusty dusty black and white
Radio with wire hanger
Antenna and no knobs
Like the toothless
Viejo who in his
Yankees cap
White sweaty
T-shirt and Guayabera
With a Panama hat
Heaves it along
Cracked concrete
Streets of the
Neighborhood
Toward the corner
Or the park
This sacred sunny
Hazy lazy
Summer day
When all you
Want to do
Is sit or play
Eating
Piraguas
All day

WATERMELON

Black rowboats
Stuck in a pink sun

Rainforest of striped skin
Smooth as a baby's
Bottom or the bald
Face of an egg

A smile for miles
All that bright pink
With black teeth

The ocean is a pink
Sponge with black
Rowboat teeth

Stuck in the
Green of your
Sweet surprising
Smile

You fill me with
Water from your
Sugar well

Each slice
Screams

The mouth of you
Becomes my mouth
As I kiss your
Endless water

Summer Sonnet on the Beach

Buckets and shovels for sandcastles you build high
Or to bury your dad from shoulders to feet
Then off to the water's edge to catch a tide
And back to mom all wet for food to eat
While the sun bakes you from high up in the sky
And the wind starts to kick sand into your eyes
As dad hands you his shades and you slap him five
Looking all cool, able to stare at the sky
Then your sister drenches you in suntan lotion
Making you shiny as a body builder
'Til you sizzle, dashing to the ocean
To cool the hot off, then run back to splash her
As she runs off giggling, stepping on towels
That aren't yours, making nearby people scowl

WEEKENDS ARE MY FAVORITE TIME

Weekends are my favorite time
When I can play hopscotch, tag,
Ride my bike, fly my kite or climb
Trees in the big old smile of the sun.

Weekends I wake real early
I don't moan and groan like on school days
That are surely a pain making me
Want to bury my head in my pillow
And shout at the alarm clock

On Saturday I get to watch cartoons
I make it to the TV before anyone else
Before Mama makes me get the broom
And keeps me busy cleaning

Up my messy room, doing other chores
Sweeping the hall, taking the trash out
All that cleaning is a major bore
It's a pain that makes me want to hide

But by twelve I get to go outside
With my friends and play
After Mama's lunch stretches my belly
I go out back or to the park the rest of the day

With Pete, Anne, Junebug and Steve
To swing on the swings and dive in the sandbox
Or laze in the front yard, watching slugs
Sucking on a dead log, trying to get on our socks

PART SIX
WORDS!
WORDS!

Lift every voice...

—James Weldon Johnson

WORDS! WORDS!

Words words
   Do their thing
Words words
   Make me sing

Words make me
   Run and jump
Words make me
   Spin and twirl

Sprint and spring
   Like a squirrel
Words fill my mouth
   'Til I have chipmunk cheeks

Words make me
   Cry or speak
Words make me
   Ring-a-ding-ding!

I see words
   Tap-tap-tap!
I hear words
   Clap-clap-clap!

Words I write
   In my book
Words from the
   Dictionary I look

Up at the sky at a plane's
   Skywriting surprise
Words words
   In the sky!

Words words on a bus
   Driving by
Words on the blackboard
   Or a billboard outside

Words in my soup
    Dangling from a teabag
Words words in the
    Classroom surrounding me

Words in my mind
    When I sleep and dream
Words running from a rained-on
    Newspaper into a black stream

Words that I speak
    All the time
Words that I rap
    Words that I rhyme

Words that shine on a
    Nickel and a dime
Words that roll around
    Bounce about

Words that make me
  Sing and shout
Words that make me
  Run and jump

Words that make my feet
  Go *thump, thump, thump*
And my rump go
  Bump, bump, bump

Words words
  Do their thing
Words words
  Make me sing

Words sprouting from a book
  Into my head
Words will live forever
  They'll never be dead

School Time Limericks

Class Time

There once was a math teacher so mean
Her cat eyeglasses were vomit green
She'd snarl at our class
Eyes squinting through glass
For not knowing 12 plus 4 was 16

Bathroom Time

The water fountain spout is too high
And stuffed with spitballs making it dry
You have to stand on a chair
Make sure you don't wet your hair
When it unsticks to squirt you in the eye

Lunchtime

This cafeteria food sure is lousy
Brillo pad burgers, stubby fries look mousy
So soggy and gray
Ketchup dry as hay
Ends up in my belly, heavy and bouncy

Playtime

Our schoolyard is a dangerous place
Without fences or trees it's a disgrace
And no places to hide
When it's snowing outside
You could catch a snowball in your face

After School

Big Bill Bruney is such a fool
He tried to chase me after school
He didn't get too far
Chugging like a broke car
And hopping a fence into a pool

MY HAIR

My hair is beautifully spun
    My hair ain't ugly

My hair is an umbrella
    Soft as a sponge

Protecting me from rain
    Reaching toward the sun

My hair takes naps
    And does what it please

My hair is a fist
    Raised high, proud as can be

My hair is a sunflower
    In full bloom

My hair is a black crown
    Shiny as the moon

My hair ain't ugly
    And don't come from Mars

My hair is a halo
    Reaching to the stars

HOW YOU MADE ME FEEL ON VALENTINE'S DAY

My heart was crushed
Like a paper cup

Kicked around
Like an empty soda can

By a gust of wind
Rattling its way

Across the rough tongue
Of the pavement

Walked on by you
Not giving me a

Valentine's Day card
But instead

Giving one to that doofus
That sits behind you

In our class
My heart feels like

It's made of glass
And you're not

Making me a card
Broke it into a

Million trillion
Sharp shark

Teeth and
Shattered wings

CLOSED BOOK BLUES

My teacher said
I wasn't curious
And I didn't know
What to do

My teacher said
I wasn't curious
And wasn't much
I could do

She said since I didn't
Read my book
I might as well
Wear it like a shoe

Said since you won't
Read that book
You might as well
Wear it like a shoe

'Cause books were
Made for reading
Not stuck on a shelf
As if it were sealed with glue

She said a book isn't
Supposed to be on a shelf
With its lips
Sealed with glue

She said books
Weren't made to be
Laying around lonely
Dusty and blue

She said you'd be the better
To pick one up
And let it take
Hold of you

My teacher said it's foolish
Not to be curious
About a closed book
That's mysterious

And I told her
I *was* curious
And I was
Nobody's fool

She said, *Oh, yeah?*
And I said, *Yeah!*
What do you think
I'm doing in school?

Then I went over
To the bookshelf
And pulled a big
Book down

Went over to the shelf
Sat a big book down
Let it grab a hold of me
'Til I couldn't put it down

WHAT I SEE ON MY WAY TO SCHOOL

Skinny trees with knobby knees
Sunlight dancing through the leaves
An old beat-up car about to sneeze

Pigeons waiting on window ledges
For me and my friends to pass
To do their business on our heads and book bags

Squirrels eating acorns, playing tag
Buses packed like sardines with people
Who don't seem too glad

Old guys in the park playing bocce ball
A younger one sitting at a chess table by himself
Waiting for a challenger to come along

A mother carrying her baby close to her chest
While trying to keep from dropping grocery bags
Rushing to catch the bus that just left

A stupid jogger wearing shorts
Who doesn't seem too worried about catching cold
When everyone else is wearing coats

Buildings that seem to look down at me
Like the principal who scrunches up his eyebrows
Into a frown when I'm late

Cars racing to beat the light
Crazy people crossing the street without looking both ways
When the light says, "Don't Walk"

Older ladies pushing laundry carts that stop to talk
Who don't relize they are standing
On a hopscotch board drawn with chalk

Coffee steaming from a paper cup
In the hands of a man coming out of the bodega
After delivering bread and picking up a newspaper

The mailman who's actually a mailwoman
Stop signs with no sign
Manhole covers that chime

Street grates that belch up puffs of smoke
Construction workers jacking up the street
Scaffolding trying to keep bricks from crushing my feet

Dogs dragging owners with their leashes
Fire hydrants afraid to peek
Ambulance siren songs not so sweet

A dizzy bumblebee on the attack
A pretty sunflower unable to fight back
A red-tailed cardinal singing, *Tweet-tweet-tweet*

My best friend in school with a fistful of candy
Like a box of crayons or a flower bouquet
The crossing guard with a big old smile for me

My Class

I love my class!
We have kids
From all over
There's Benny
Who's Japanese
But doesn't know karate
Who shares his Manga books
With me, making
Drawings
For my stories

There's Michelle Muhammad
Who's from Palestine;
Kiko from the Philipines
Whose break dance moves
Are so right on time
He could bust a backspin
While holding up a dime
In each hand,
Rocking a headstand

Then there's Martin
From Martinique
Who is the best at
Math and fixes
Everybody's computer
Mischa from Sarajevo
Who learned English
From watching TV
Listening to CDs
Reading books
Like they were going
Out of style

Our teacher,
Mr. Kim, is Korean
He was born
In the Bronx near
Yankee Stadium.
He's so cool
He even lets us write reports
On our favorite comic books

I love my class
We have people
From so many places
Like Italy, Ireland,
El Salvador and Nigeria.
By the time I reach
The fifth grade
I might end up
Learning the coolest slang
Words in at least six
Or seven languages

auTHOR's noTes:
poeTRY FORms & PROMPTs
useD in
THe PResiDenT LOOKs LiKe me

poeTRY FORms

Blues Poem — an African American form that originates in the oral and musical traditions of the blues. African American poets Langston Hughes and Sterling Brown helped to popularize blues poetry. The blues handles serious issues in a humorous and/or ironic way. Blues poems often deal with struggles and overcoming hardships. Formally, blues stanzas begin with a statement in the first line, followed by a variation of that statement on the second line and a humorous or ironic alternative on the third line.

Example: "Closed Book Blues"

Concrete Poem — a poem that graphically (visually) depicts the theme or action of a poem's subject or content.

Example: "Break Dancer"

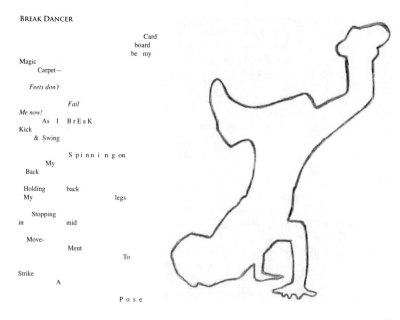

BREAK DANCER

Epistolary Poems — are written in letter format. In epistolary poetry, you can also use the form of a diary, journal or blog entry. The epistolary poem is one that lends itself to easy flowing free writing and intimacy of thoughts and feelings. You can write an epistolary poem to anyone you'd like and even invent characters, as well. In this regard, pay close attention to the specific way your character would communicate (write or speak), for this reveals certain aspects of a character's background and personality.

      Example: "Dear God"

Haiku — a Japanese style poem consisting of seventeen syllables distributed over three lines. The object is to focus on creating rich imagery and have the last line be revelatory (surprising).

      Example: "Hurricane Katrina Haiku," and
"Haiku Bless You"

Limerick — a humorous poem invented in the 1800s in England and made popular in Ireland. It consists of a stanza of five lines, three beats per line, and an end rhyme pattern of *aabba*.

      Example: "School Time Limericks"

List Poem — a poem that consists of listing items, images, memories and metaphors to create an overall collage effect. The idea is to focus on creating rich imagery filled with specificity. Albert Einstein once said, "God is in the details." In poetry, beauty is in the details. Try to think of an experience or a memory and write down a list of all the verbal images it may evoke. You can also try using a photograph as a prompt for your list.

      Example: "My Favorite Things" and
"What I See on My Way to School"

Odes — poems of praise written to a place or thing. In the ode, one usually praises an object or thing using images, metaphors and similes that are rich and unique. Instead of focusing on what that object is, the idea is to create images of what that object may resemble or how it may make you feel.

> Example: "Ode to Potato Chips," "Piragua," "Fall,"
> "Winter," "Spring," and "Watermelon"

Praise Poems — derive from the African tradition. Similar to an ode, a praise poem focuses specifically on a person rather than an object. The idea is to think about what that person means to you and how he or she makes you feel, using unique, rich imagery, thus giving the reader or listener a heightened sense of the subject being praised.

> Example: "The President Looks Like Me," "Uncle Pepe,"
> "Sundays," and "My Class"

Sonnets — fourteen line poems of varying rhyme schemes that have ten syllables per line. The word sonnet comes from the Italian word *sonetto*, which means little song. The sonnet, with its rhyme pattern and ten-syllable line, has its own built-in, song-like lyricism. I find it easier to anticipate my end rhymes and write lines out of order; then piece the poem together to make some sort of sense of the entire sonnet.

> Example: "Stand-in Father" and "Summer Sonnet on the
> Beach"

Tanka — a Japanese style poem that extends Haiku by two extra lines of seven syllables each. Tanka consists of thirty-one syllables distributed over five lines. The object is to focus on creating rich imagery and have the last line be revelatory or surprising.

> Example: "Tanka for My Dad"

POETRY PROMPTS

"I Am From" is a poem in which one begins with the refrain, "I Am From". The words are used to depict where the author is from. In this poem the objective is not merely to state where you live or where you were born, but to explore your cultural roots, your family, friends, neighborhood, your likes and dislikes to compile a poem that expresses who you are in a myriad of ways.

    Example: "I Am From"

"Grandma's Hands" is a poem inspired by a popular song of the same title written by Bill Withers. In this poem the author describes someone close to him or her by focusing on a part of the subject's body, or something memorable about that person, in order to give a heightened sense of the person. For instance, you can write a poem about your father's hat or great grandmother's cane; or your mother's perfume or pearls. With this device, the reader or listener discovers so much about an individual through objects attributed to him or her.

    Example: "Grandma's Hands"

"Hip Hop You Don't Stop" is what I call a "Fortune Cooke Poem". Here the poem derives from the message contained in the cookie. The line must either appear in the title, body, an epigraph or is used as inspiration for the poem. A Fortune Cookie Poem is a fun and tasty poetry promp that would be great for a classrom activity or as a party game.

    Example: "Hip Hop You Don't Stop"

WHAT KIND OF VOCABULARY
IS USED IN THE POEMS?

"THE PRESIDENT LOOKS LIKE ME"

B-ball: slang for basketball
Mad cool: very cool

"RHYME TIME"

PB&J: peanut butter and jelly

"PIRAGUA"

Piragua: shaved ice served in paper cones or cups of
flavored syrup

"MY FAVORITE THINGS" (The title of a popular American song)

Cain and Abel: Figures in the Bible's The Old Testament
Falafel: ground chickpeas formed into a ball and fried,
usually served in a pita which acts as a pocket or
wrapped in a flatbread.
Headstand: a move or position in break dancing
Jonah: Biblical figure in the The Old Testament
Manga: Japanese graphic novels
Matzo ball soup: Jewish soup made without yeast
Merengue: Dominican style music
Mosque: A Muslim place of worship
Mulligatawny soup: Indian soup made with lentils and tomato
Picante: hot sauce
Platanos: green bananas
Salsa music: Spanish style music from Cuba, Puerto Rico and New
York City
Samosas: Indian potato fritters
Spades: a playing card game
Timbs: Timberland shoes/boots
Yankees: The New York Yankees baseball team

"CARDBOARD CANTICLE"

Canticle: a hymn taken from the Bible
Deejaying: playing records and making music by blending two
different song lines from two different records.
Doofus: slang for fool
Johnnie pump: slang for fire hydrant

HISTORICAL FIGURES

Albizu Campos: A leading Puerto Rican political activist who fought for Puerto Rican independence

Cesar Chavez: A Mexican-American activist who fought for farm workers' rights

Crazy Horse: Native American war leader of the Oglala Lakota tribe

Malcolm X: Dynamic and influential African-American leader, formerly a member of The Nation of Islam, who advovated Black pride and preached self-determination

President Barack Obama: The first African-America president of the United States of America

Supreme Court Justice Sonia Sotomayor: The first Puerto Rican and Latina Supreme Court Justice of the United States

MUSICAL FIGURES

James Brown: Pioneering singer, dancer and recording artist known as "The Godfather of Soul"

John Coltrane: Innovative African-American jazz saxophonist and composer

Common: African-American rap artist and actor from Chicago known for conscious lyrics and his affiliation with Phildelphia rap group, "The Roots"

Celia Cruz: Pioneering Cuban singer known as "The Queen of Salsa"

Aretha Franklin: Pioneering African-American singer known as "The Queen of Soul"

Michael Jackson: Pioneering African-American singer, songwriter and dancer known as "The King of Pop"

Talib Kweli: Brooklyn-born, politically conscious rap artist and activist who formed the group "Black Star" with fellow rap artist Mos Def

Lupe: (Lupe Fiasco) A politically conscious rap artist and social activist whose parents were Black Panthers

Bob Marley: Jamaicn-born musician and leader of the Reggae group "The Wailers." His music helped to shed light on plight of poor people in Jamaica and around the world.

Mos Def: Also known as "Yasiin Bey" is an outspoken African-American rap artist and actor, who along with Talib Kweli formed the rap group "Black Star"

Tito Puente: Pioneering Puerto Rican Salsa percussionist, musician, and composer who helped to create Latin jazz with musician Dizzie Gillespie

Sade: Nigerian singer and songwriter of R&B, alternative and pop music

Tupac: (Tupac Shakur) An outspokent African-American rap artist and actor

Stevie Wonder: Major African-American musician, singer, songwriter of R&B and popular music who fought for recognition of Dr. Martin Luther King's birthday as a national holiday

ABOUT THE AUTHOR

Tony Medina was born and raised in the Bronx and spent much of his adult life living in Harlem. The author and editor of sixteen books for adults and young readers, Medina is a two-time winner of the Paterson Prize for Books for Young People for *DeShawn Days* (2001) and *I and I, Bob Marley* (2009). His anthology, *Bum Rush the Page: A Def Poetry Jam*, was a *Washington Post* Best Book of the Year (2001). Medina's latest collections of poetry include *An Onion of Wars*, *Broke on Ice* and *My Old Man Was Always on the Lam*, a finalist for the 2011 Paterson Poetry Prize.

An advisory editor for Nikki Giovanni's *Hip Hop Speaks to Children*, he is featured in the poetry documentary *Furious Flower II* and the *Encyclopedia of Hip Hop Literature*. Medina, who holds an MA and PhD from Binghamton University, is the first Professor of Creative Writing at Howard University. He has read his work, lectured and conducted workshops extensively across the country and abroad. His poetry, fiction and essays appear in over ninety anthologies and publications. He is also the author of *Follow-up Letters to Santa from Kids Who Never Got a Response* (Just Us Books, 2003).